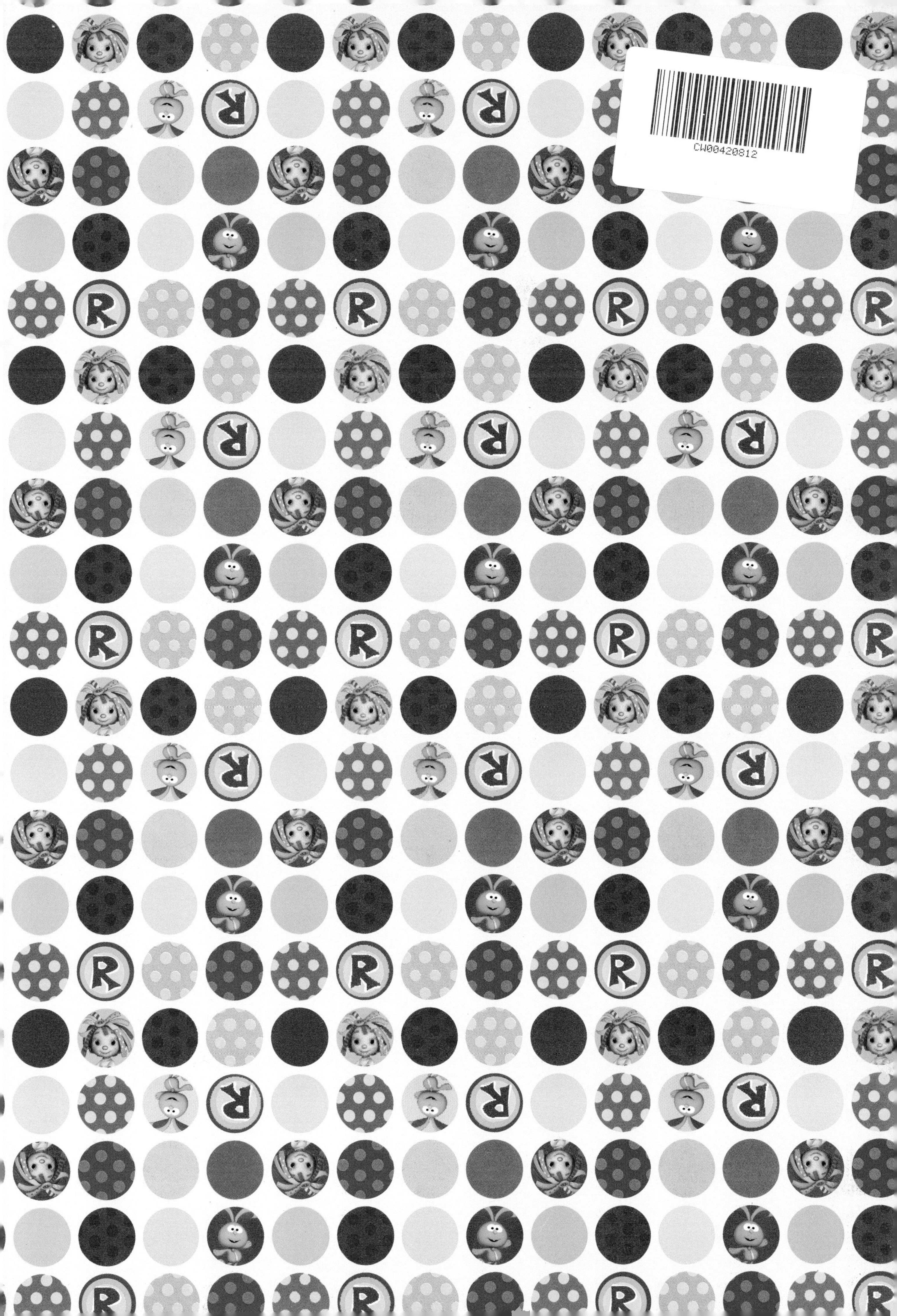

Friends together!

Pedigree

Published 2011. Pedigree Books Ltd, Beech Hill House, Walnut Gardens, Exeter, Devon EX4 4DH
books@pedigreegroup.co.uk | www.pedigreebooks.com

£7.99

Welcome to my World

Hello! I'm Rosie.

I'm really glad you've dropped by as I love to make new friends. I hope you can stay and play a while. You can? That's fantastic!

In this brilliant annual I'll introduce you to all my friends - Big Bear, Will, Holly, Oakley, Bluebird.... and, of course, Raggles.

Do you like colouring? I love it! You'll find lots of fun colouring and drawing activities in this book, plus games and puzzles.... oh, and stories to read about my amazing adventures. So, come on! Let's go and explore....

Love Rosie

Everything about...
Rosie
R
Name: Rosie
Lives: The Playhouse
Best friend: Raggles
Favourite thing to do: Play with all my friends, ride on the Twooter, whizz down the Playhouse slide
Things I'm good at: Having great ideas and helping my friends
Yummiest snack: Bozberry muffins or apple and strawberry crumble
How many buttons can you count on the page?

Everything's Fun with Friends

Everything about...
Raggles
Name: Raggles
Lives: The Playhouse
Best friend: Rosie
Favourite thing to do: Snooze in my hammock, do tricks with my yo-yo, play my penny whistle, eat yummy food
Things I'm good at: Hopping, doing the Raggles Wriggle, telling funny jokes
Yummiest snack: Banana and honey sandwiches
What kind of an animal is Raggles? Can you write the word here?
_ _ _ _ _ _

Get cracking and colour me in!

Good idea Rosie, good idea!

Sunshine and Shadows

When the sun is high in the sky your shadow comes out to play. It looks just like you, but can you spot Rosie and her pals from their shadows? Write the letter in the box next to the right picture.

Can you finish the sentences below by choosing the correct word from the list? Now write the missing word in each box.

Holly's bow is Shiny

Stripy Spotty Shiny

Bluebird's tail is Yellow

Red Blue Yellow

Finished? Raggles says:

"Pat yourself on the back and say... 'Well done me!'"

Speedy
Spot The Difference

A

Whhhheeeeeeeeeeeeee!

Rosie and Raggles love whizzing around on the Twooter. But can you spot five differences between picture A and picture B? The answers are on page 77.

Happy Holly's

Don't you just love making Daisy chains? I do. They look really pretty as bracelets or crowns.

Can you answer the questions below to fill in the flower path? The last letter of the first word is also the first letter of the second word, and so on.

1. Bluebird lives in a ...?
2. Rosie loves to race on this ...?
3. Rosie's best friend is called ...?
4. Holly's bow is ...?
5. Bluebird's beak is pink and ...?

Daisy Chain
1
2
3
4
5
N _ S T W
_ S _ _
L _ L O O O
G _ _ _
_ Y T T
_ R _

Rosie a
Hello again!
How are you enjoying my Annual?
Now we're friends, why don't you draw yourself next to me in the picture frame?
Don't we look great!
Love Rosie.

nd Me

Everything about...

Bluebird

Name: Bluebird

Lives: In a nest in Oakley's branches

Best friend: Oakley

Favourite thing to do: Sing my dawn chorus, perform magic, talk, talk talk!

Things I'm good at: Aerial flying displays, building nests, getting some beauty sleep

Yummiest snack: Large juicy apples

Bluebird loves to fly high in the sky. The pictures here show other things that fly. Can you circle the object that cannot fly?

Everyone knows I have the most beautiful feathers around. You'll need your brightest blues and yummiest yellows to colour me in!
Coooo-eeee! It's only me!

Raggles The Reporter

One sunny day, Rosie was outside oiling her Twooter. **"Do you like your Twooter Rosie?"** Raggles asked. "Of course I do!" Rosie answered. **"Do you prefer to ride it on your own, or with me?"** Raggles asked. Rosie was puzzled by all the questions. What was Raggles up to?

"I'm writing a newspaper, The Playhouse Bugle, and you are my first story," the bunny announced. He read out what he had written. It was all about Rosie oiling the Twooter's wheels to make it go faster. It wasn't very interesting.

"I can't think of anything else to write!" Raggles groaned. Rosie had some good advice. **"I'm sure you will, you just haven't found it yet. Write something that everyone will want to read!"** she suggested. Raggles decided to find the perfect story.

Raggles walked through the orchard looking for ideas. He saw a bird sitting in a tree. Was that interesting? No! He noticed the grass was long. Not interesting! Then he heard footsteps. It was Holly. Raggles hid behind a tree.

"Big Bear's apple is perfectly ripe!" Holly cried as she picked the shiny red fruit. **"He's in for a big surprise!"** she smiled skipping off happily. Raggles gasped. **"Big Bear in for nasty surprise when Holly takes his apple,"** he wrote.

Next Raggles came across Bluebird who was trying to magic a nest she'd built on the ground fly up into a tree. The magic didn't work. **"That's the problem with nests, so unhelpful, and this tree is silly,"** she cawed. Raggles wrote: Bluebird says trees are silly! **"That's a brilliant story!"** he said.

A little later Raggles came across Will on Oakley's Hill. As he watched, Will kicked his football hard up the hill. Bonk! It hit Oakley on the nose. **"Ouch!'** Oakley said as the ball rolled back down the hill followed by a laughing Will.

"Will kicks ball at Oakley's nose and runs away laughing! What a great story!" Raggles said. As he headed back to the Playhouse Raggles didn't see Will walking back up the hill with the football. **"That was a brilliant save, you're one great goalie!"** Will told Oakley.

Raggles worked on his newspaper all morning. Rosie asked to peek at his stories but the stubborn little rabbit said she'd have to wait. Rosie waited for several hours until Raggles came out, holding several copies of The Playhouse Bugle.

"Show me then!" Rosie said excitedly. Raggles insisted they had to deliver all the other copies first. The pair sped off around the park on the Twooter and gave their friends papers. The last delivery was to Oakley.

"Hurry up Oakley, I want a read," Rosie laughed. **"It says here Bluebird thinks trees are silly,"** moaned Oakley. Rosie said Raggles wouldn't have written that if he hadn't heard it. Will, Holly, Bluebird and Big Bear approached holding newspapers and looked very cross.

Rosie read for a minute and then shook her head. **"Oh Raggles. What have you done?"** she asked. **"I did not say all trees were silly, just the tree I was trying to magic my nest into!"** cawed Bluebird.

"I didn't kick the ball at Oakley's nose and run away laughing. He was being a goalie!" said Will. **"You said I took Big Bear's apple!"** said Rosie. Big Bear held up his paw containing the apple. **"She picked it for me,"** he said.

The friends surrounded Raggles and threw their newspapers at his feet. **"I'm really sorry,"** sighed Raggles. A tear rolled down his cheek. Rosie put her arm around her friend to comfort him.

"I'm sure Raggles didn't mean to upset everyone," Rosie told the group. Raggles nodded. **"Maybe the newspaper wasn't such a good idea,"** he sniffed. **"It's a wonderful idea, Raggles, it's just the stories need to be more fun!"** Rosie explained.

By the end of the day Raggles had produced a new and improved Playhouse Bugle complete with funny pictures and jokes. **"This is the best newspaper I have ever read!"** Oakley exclaimed. **"Well done Raggles!"** smiled Rosie.

Vvroooooooooooooooooooooooooooom!
Rosie, Raggles and Will are racing round the park to the Playhouse. Will may think he's the champion, but can Rosie and Raggles pip him to the post?

1

2 Help Little Bear climb Oakley's Hill. **Move forward 2 spaces.**

3

11 Aaachooo! Oakley sneezed **Everyone bac[k] to the start.**

12 Boing! Boing! Slow down to let the Acorns pass. **The other player catches up to you.**

13

14 Your wheel falls off. **Miss a turn.**

15

16 Cawww! Bluebird says you must **move back 3** if your name contains the letter E.

17

To play you will need:
• A dice • Two counters (you could use different coins or coloured scraps of paper)

4

5 You stop for a swing. **Miss a turn.**

6

7 Big Bear is snoozing on the path. **Miss a go while you move him.**

8 Holly wants you to duet with her. Sing a song and **Move forward 4 spaces.**

9

10

18 Saffie says count to 10 to **move forward 1 space.**

19

20 **You've won!**

Acorn Hide and Seek

Those Little Acorns bounce around so much it's hard to keep up with them. Today they're playing hide and seek in the garden. Can you help find them? You'll have to look carefully to spot them. Colour in an apple every time you spot one.

Design a nest for Bluebird

Bluebird likes to look her best,
She wants to have the coolest nest.
Can you draw her a comfy bed,
Where she can lay down her proud head?
Now use your colours red, blue, green,
It's the best picture ever seen!

Everything about...
Big Bear
Name: Big Bear
Lives: Big Bear's Den
Best friend: Holly
Favourite thing to do: Nap against a tree-trunk, grow flowers and vegetables, pom-de-pom
Things I'm good at: Giving Big Bear hugs, cooking up feasts for all my friends, helping others
Yummiest snack: Pancakes with syrup
How many paws does Big Bear have? Circle a paw print for each one.
34

Ho! Ho!
My fur is blue don't you know! But don't forget a brown pencil or crayon for my favourite jumper!
Pom de pom de pom...

How to Teach a Bear

One day Rosie and Raggles heard a knock at the door. It was Big Bear and he looked worried. **"You look like you've lost an apple and found a pip!"** Raggles said. Big Bear had a letter. **"Dear Big Bear, Please can you come to my Palace for tea. From, The Queen,"** the letter said. **"You should be excited!"** Rosie told Big Bear, taking his paw and skipping round the room. But Big Bear was worried. He'd never had tea with a Queen before and he didn't know what to do.

Rosie told her friend not to worry. **"You've come to the right place,"** she said. **"We're going to teach you how to have tea with the Queen… aren't we Raggles?"** The little rabbit nodded. **"First, you have to dress right,"** said Rosie, who gave him an orange top hat.

Next, Rosie lent Big Bear some purple earmuffs. He still looked unhappy. **"I'm sorry, but I don't like any of them,"** he said. **"What do you like then?"** Rosie asked. Big Bear pulled at the hem of his favourite brown jumper. **"This,"** he said.

"It's not exactly smart, is it?" asked Raggles. Big Bear was upset. He loved his jumper. **"Hmm. Wait there,"** said Rosie as she ran home. A few moments later she returned with a jaunty, red bow-tie. **"Perfect!"** said Raggles. Big Bear agreed. He did look smart.

"Now you've got to walk right," said Rosie. Big Bear was confused. **"She means you have to walk tall,"** said Raggles. Big Bear tried his best but he still loped like a bear. **"I'll soon have him walking like a Prince,"** Rosie giggled as she gave Big Bear a book to balance on his head while he walked.

Big Bear walked up the hill towards Oakley. He was concentrating so hard on walking tall that he didn't see Will hiding in the bushes. **"Ha, Ha! This is my best trick ever!"** Will chuckled. **"Having tea with the Queen! As if!"** Giggling to himself he pulled out a pad and pencil and began to write Holly an invite to the palace.
Rosie, Raggles and Big Bear had no idea what naughty Will was planning. They were having a tea-party so Big Bear could practise his manners. Big Bear held his teacup daintily but gulped his tea down very noisily. **"Great slurping!"** Raggles laughed. **"You always slurp when you meet the Queen!"** Rosie added. Oakley said it was important to speak clearly.

Big Bear did his best to say each word correctly. At first he got muddled but finally he said them right. **"I think you are ready to have tea with the Queen!"** Raggles smiled. Holly ran over, clutching a card which said. **"Dear Holly, Please can you come to my Palace for tea. From, The Queen."**
There was a crashing of branches and Bluebird landed with a thud. **"What's the rush, Bluebird?"** Raggles asked. **"I've only been invited to tea by the Queen,"** she said. **"I knew it was only a matter of time before I'd be perched at the top table."**

Rosie looked at Bluebird's invite. Then she asked Big Bear and Holly for theirs. **"What is it, Rosie?"** Raggles asked. **"I recognise this handwriting,"** she said. **"I know who wrote these."** The writing was exactly the same on each card. They were all from Will.
Holly, Bluebird and Big Bear had never looked so disappointed. **"But I've had a wash!"** groaned Big Bear. **"And I've polished my beak!"** cawed Bluebird. **"He's gone too far this time,"** Oakley grumbled. Rosie agreed. She led everyone down the hill, to have tea with the Queen!

The group met Will in the playground. **"Where are you going?"** he laughed. **"To have tea with the Queen!"** Holly and Big Bear said. Will looked puzzled. **"But I was tricking you,"** he said.
"There's nothing funny about having tea with her Royal Highness!" Bluebird squawked. Will asked to go, but Holly said he wasn't invited.
When Big Bear pressed Rosie's doorbell Raggles-the-butler answered. **"Her Royal Highness is waiting for you inside,"** he said. Queen Rosie was sitting at the table wearing her crown. **"Thank you for coming to my palace,"** she said. The table full of cupcakes looked wonderful.

There was a knock at the door. It was Will. **"Hello Raggles,"** he said. **"That's Sir Raggles,"** Raggles corrected. **"Sir Raggles, can I have tea with Her Royal Highness Rosie, please?"** Will asked. Raggles let Will in. **"On one condition,"** he said. Will was allowed to join the tea party – as a waiter, serving lemonade to the friends he'd tried to trick.
That night Rosie and Raggles snuggled up in bed to talk about their day. **"Wouldn't it be great if you were a real Queen!"** Raggles said. **"I could play the games I liked, when I liked, with whom I liked...**
... I'd always win because I'd make up all the rules," said Rosie. **"You could wear a big crown and we could have a cake factory,"** Rosie laughed. **"What about a talking blue rabbit?"** she asked. **"There's no such thing,"** said Raggles.

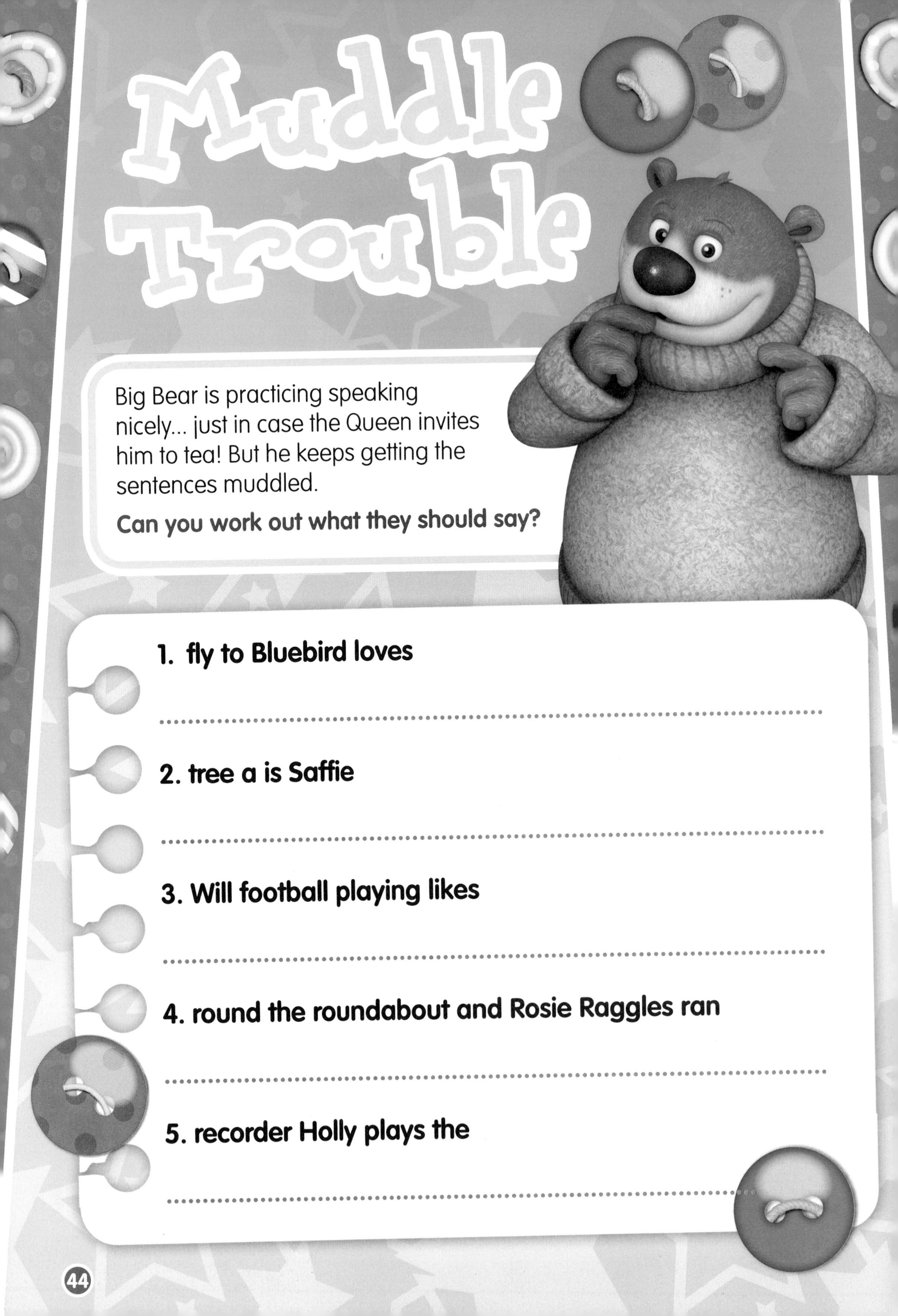

Muddle Trouble

Big Bear is practicing speaking nicely... just in case the Queen invites him to tea! But he keeps getting the sentences muddled.

Can you work out what they should say?

1. fly to Bluebird loves

....

2. tree a is Saffie

....

3. Will football playing likes

....

4. round the roundabout and Rosie Raggles ran

....

5. recorder Holly plays the

....

Amazing Maze

One of the best things about Rosie's World is the maze. It's so easy to get lost and such fun to find your way out again. Help Little Bear find his way through to meet Big Bear and Bluebird by tracing the path with your finger.

Everything about...

Oakley

Name: Oakley

Lives: Oakley's Hill

Best friend: The Little Acorns

Favourite thing to do: Feel the wind in my leaves, share fun and laughter with my friends

Things I'm good at: Telling stories, listening and giving advice, being goalie for Will

Yummiest snack: Water from the ground through my roots

How will you colour me in? My trunk is always brown, but my leaves are green in summer and reds, oranges and browns in autumn!
How many of Oakley's leaves have fallen around these two pages?
Let me tell you a story!

Oakley and the Big Sneeze

One morning Raggles was in Rosie's house trying to build the tallest brick tower when... **"AACCHHOOO!"** An enormous sneeze blew in through the window and knocked the tower down. Who had sneezed so hard?

It was Oakley! The tree had bleary eyes and a twitchy nose. Bluebird swooped down. **"You, my dear Oakley, have a cold,"** she squawked. Little Bear thought the sneezing was funny. The oak tree didn't want to sneeze, he couldn't stop.

"AAACCHHOOOOOO!" This time the sneeze was so gigantic it knocked Little Bear off his feet and rolling down the hill. He landed in a very muddy puddle and was filthy and a little bit smelly. **"It's the bathtub for you!"** Big Bear said.

Rosie and Raggles arrived to see what was happening. **"Don't come any closer! He has gale force sneezes,"** said Bluebird. Oakley's next giant sneeze blew Rosie and Raggles down to the playground.

Rosie and Raggles walked back up the hill and met Will who was dragging his kite behind him. **"Your kite's on the ground,"** Raggles told him. **"I know, no wind!"** Will puffed. **"Maybe we can help,"** said Rosie. Will was confused!

Up the hill, Oakley let rip with another sneeze. Before Will could ask what the noise was, his kite was lifted by the rush of air. **"Wow!"** he laughed, as his kite took off. Little Bear wanted the kite. **"Mine!"** he said, holding out his paw.

"Here you go then. Hold on tight," Will said, handing Little Bear the kite string. Before long another huge sneeze exploded from Oakley. **"Look out everyone!"** Bluebird warned, flying upwards to avoid the giant gust of air that followed.

Will, Big Bear, Rosie and Raggles held on to each other but Holly tumbled over and back down the hill. She was fine, but where was Little Bear? From above they heard his tiny voice – and saw him dangling on the end of the kite string.

"Little Bear!" Rosie gasped. **"Hold on tight!"** Big Bear cried. But Little Bear just thought it was fantastic to be flying so high. There was no time to lose. **"Will, get the Go-Speeder. Raggles, get the Twooter. Follow that kite!"** said Rosie.

Will and Raggles sped along through the trees after Little Bear. Will was driving the Go-Speeder with Holly as passenger while Rosie and Raggles were on the Twooter. Big Bear followed behind in the Go-Pod with Bluebird.

They travelled miles along tracks and over meadows before the kite dropped into a wood. **"We'll never find him, there are too many trees,"** croaked Bluebird. But Rosie told everyone to be quiet and they heard a sweet lullaby.

The friends followed the sound of the lullaby and found Little Bear safe in the branches of Saffie the cedar tree. **"Thank you Saffie,"** sighed Big Bear with relief, as he reached up to get Little Bear.

"He knows he can drop by any time," Saffie whispered. Rosie smiled gratefully. **"Saffie, can you help us? Oakley can't stop sneezing,"** she told the tree. "**Hmmm, well one person's ice cream is another's spinach!"** said Saffie.

"You mean it might be something that we like, but Oakley doesn't?" asked Rosie. **"We may know what's making you sneeze,"** Rosie told Oakley. **"What?"** asked Bluebird. **"You,"** said Rosie. "**Every time Oakley sneezed you were flying round him. I think it's your feathers!"**

Bluebird was horrified. **"Everyone loves my feathers! They even smell wonderful now Holly's sprayed them with her perfume!"** squawked Bluebird. **"Perfume?"** Rosie asked. Holly squirted scent in the air and Oakley was off again.

"I'm sorry Oakley, I never meant to tickle your nose," said Holly. Oakley smiled and said he'd had a sensitive nose since he was a sapling. **"Pheew! I can smell something now,"** he said. It was Little Bear, covered in dirt. It was time for a bath!

Aaaachh is Whose

oooWhose
5
4
E
D
Uh Oh! Oakley has sneezed so hard he's blown away all his friends' favourite things. Can you match each lost object to its owner? Use a coloured pencil or crayon to draw a line between the two.

Copy Colour

The grass and plants on Oakley's Hill are full of colour – but can you make Rosie and her friends even brighter? Use the small picture below to help you colour in the main picture using your pencils and crayons. You can even use different colours to make the picture look a little bit different?

What Colour?

Can you say what colours these objects are in the picture?

1. Holly's dress is ____

2. Rosie's shoes are ___

3. Bluebird's beak is ____ and______

4. Will's trousers are ____

Kite Chaos

Big Bear, Little Bear, Raggles and Will have been flying kites, but their strings have got tangled. Can you work out which colour kite they are each flying? Colour the square next to their picture with the same colour as their kite.

Let's Fly!

Did you like the kites Rose and her friend flew on Oakley's Hill? You did? So did we! Here's a simple step-by-step guide for you to make your own kite!

Take care
Always ask an adult for help when using sharp scissors or knives.

You will need:

Cardboard or heavy duty paper • Sticky tape • Thin garden canes, or wooden doweling • Long length of string • Ruler • Scissors

What to do:

1. Cut two lengths of cane, one 40cm (16in) and the other 60cm (24in).
2. Mark the shorter cane at the halfway point. Mark the longer piece a third down from one end.
3. Place the canes one on top of the other, where the two marks touch, to form a cross. This is the frame of your kite.
4. Fasten the two canes together with strong sticky tape or string.
5. Put a small groove into both end of both canes. Then put some string in the notch at the top of the kite frame (the top of the cross) and wind it around the top of the rod.
6. Now take the string around the frame, passing it into the grooves you have cut in the ends of each cane.
7. When you get back to the top of the frame, tie the two string ends together in a secure knot.
8. Put your frame on top of the paper or cardboard. Cut out the shape of the kite leaving about 12mm (half an inch) extra paper or card all the way round.
9. Fold the paper or card over the string and then tape down the edges all around. Make sure the paper totally covers the paper or card.
10. Tie a length of string to each end of the shorter rod. This should be a bit longer than the rod. Tie string to each end of the longer rod, also making this longer than the rod.
11. Hold these strings at the front of the kite and where they overlap tie them together. This is where you attach the string for flying.
12. Attach your long length of string and you are ready to fly!

You can make your kite fly better by giving it a tail of several ribbons.

Fly your kit in an open space, not near trees or overhead wires.

Decorate your kite by sticking on pictures of Rosie and her friends – or drawing them yourself.

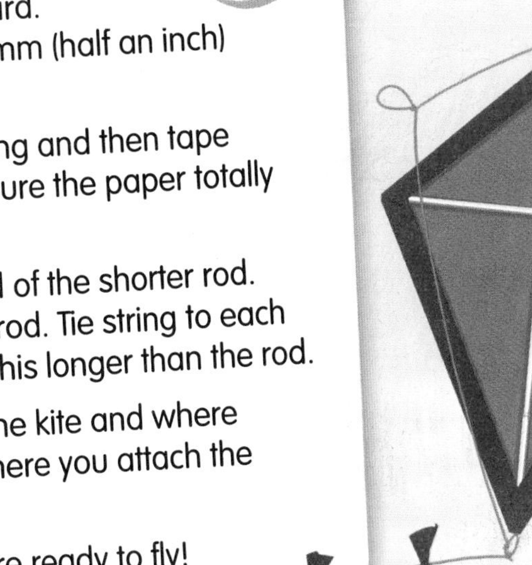

Everything about...

Will

Name: Will

Lives: Will and Holly's house

Best friend: Oakley

Favourite thing to do: Race really fast in the Go-speeder, play football

Things I'm good at: My football rocket shot, playing jokes on people, building things

Yummiest snack: Bozberryade

Holly

Name: Holly

Lives: Will and Holly's house

Best friend: Rosie

Favourite thing to do: Swing on the swing pods, painting and drawing

Things I'm good at: Singing and dancing, making things for all my friends, baking cakes and cookies

Yummiest snack: Fairy cakes

Whooaaa!!!

Hey there!
Bet you can't colour me in! My t-shirt is racing-car red to match my Go-speeder

Do you like my pretty pink dress and spotty bow? Can you colour them in lovely shades of pink and purple?

Oooh! I'll help!

The Last Snowball

It was Spring and Rosie had spent the morning sticking photos of the winter snow into her album. She glued down the last photograph that showed her friends making a snowman on Oakley Hill, and rushed to the window.

"Good thing we made the most of the snow. Look at that sunshine Raggles!" said Rosie. **"Awww – It's nearly gone,"** he said sadly, looking at the green meadows and the patches of remaining snow. He hadn't had a chance to make a snow rabbit! **"Let's show everyone the snow photos,"** she said, grabbing the album and pulling Raggles outside.

Rosie and Raggles ran up Oakley Hill. **"Hello Oakley! Look what I've got!"** said Rosie. **"Don't we look marvellous!"** chuckled Oakley, looking at the pictures of his friends in the snow. **"I'm glad Spring has sprung – everything is growing,"** he said. **"Apart from our snowman!"** said Raggles looking at the melting pile of snow.
Oakley noticed Big Bear was missing from the photographs. **"He was sleeping, remember we couldn't get him to wake up!"** said Raggles. Big Bear always slept through winter.

At that moment a loud snoring could be heard from inside Big Bear's house. Then his bear-shaped alarm clock went off. Big Bear snuffled, turned over and opened one eye. He stretched and picked up his alarm clock.

"That was a nice, long sleep," he said, clambering out of bed. He pulled on his favourite jumper and blinked in the sunshine on his porch. **"I wonder what everyone's been up to? I hope I didn't miss much,"** he said as he headed towards the playground.

Rosie, Will and Holly were already there, looking through the photo album. **"Look at me sledging!"** Will said. **"And, look at our snow angels,"** Holly added. Raggles was trying to make a sand rabbit but the sand just wouldn't stick together.
The friends laughed about how Bluebird had pounded everyone during the snowball fight. **"Come and see our snow photos,"** Holly said to Big Bear. **"Did it snow?"** he asked. **"It was this deep, we did snowballing and sledging,"** crowed Bluebird. Big Bear looked very disappointed at having missed all the fun, but Rosie had a plan to cheer him up.

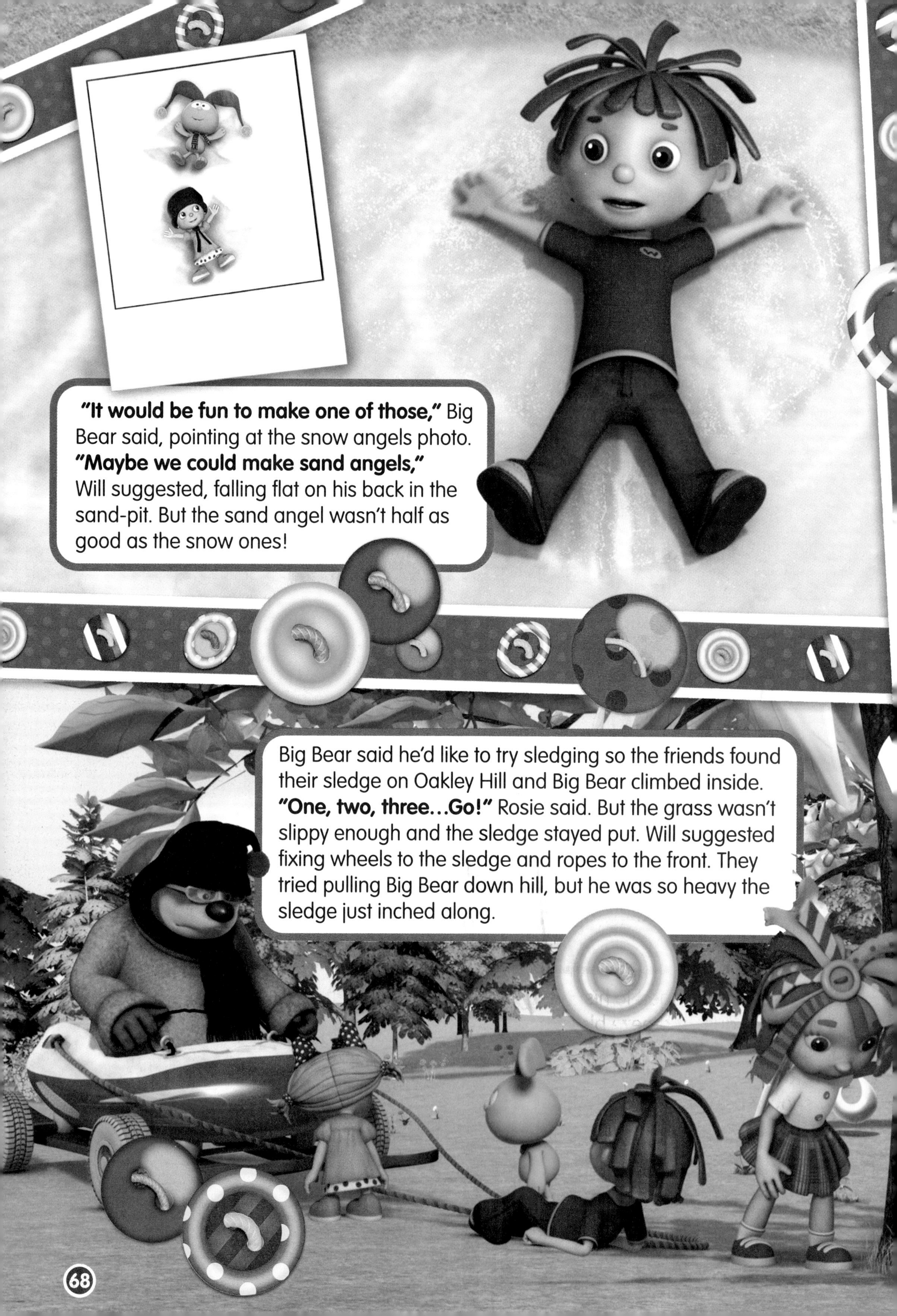

"It would be fun to make one of those," Big Bear said, pointing at the snow angels photo. **"Maybe we could make sand angels,"** Will suggested, falling flat on his back in the sand-pit. But the sand angel wasn't half as good as the snow ones!

Big Bear said he'd like to try sledging so the friends found their sledge on Oakley Hill and Big Bear climbed inside. **"One, two, three...Go!"** Rosie said. But the grass wasn't slippy enough and the sledge stayed put. Will suggested fixing wheels to the sledge and ropes to the front. They tried pulling Big Bear down hill, but he was so heavy the sledge just inched along.

"It's no good. I can't pull any more," Will said. Raggles was panting and even Rosie had to admit that no snow meant no sledging. Big Bear looked very sad. **"Maybe I didn't miss so much,"** he said. **"It's just snow,"** nodded Rosie. **"Just snow? How can you say that? It was magical!"** said Bluebird. Big Bear looked more upset than ever.
As Big Bear trudged to his house a gust of breeze blew the trees and blossom fell around them. It looked like snow. Rosie whispered in Will's ear. **"Brilliant!"** said Will.

Will and Holly went to find Big Bear as she and Raggles ran back to their melting snowman. **"We're too late!"** Raggles groaned, picking up the carrot nose and twig arms. **"There's just enough,"** Rosie said, scooping snow into her hat.
They arrived at the orchard to find Will, Holly and Big Bear – his eyes shut – under the trees. **"Now!"** Rosie shouted and Bluebird jumped up and down on the tree, causing the blossom to fall around Big Bear. Big Bear opened his eyes. **"Wow!"** he cried. **"And we've brought you this,"** Rosie said, handing Big Bear his very own snowball. Big Bear said he'd keep it forever, but he tripped over the sledge and whacked Bluebird on the beak. **"Bull's Eye!"** screeched Bluebird. Rosie photographed the moment.

That night Rosie smiled as she added the Big Bear snow-blossom photo to her winter album. **"I'm so glad Big Bear got to join in the snow, aren't you Raggles?"** she asked the rabbit. There was no answer, Raggles wasn't in the playhouse.
The door suddenly flew open and there was Raggles. He was wearing the snowman's woolly hat and scarf, had the carrot tied to his nose and was holding the two twigs for arms. **"Ta da!"** he cried. Rosie smiled and took a photo of her grinning friend. Big Bear had the last snowball but Raggles was the last snow rabbit.

Five Friends
Five good friends are hiding in this picture. Use your pen or pencil to join the dots and discover their identities. Then use your pencils or crayons to colour in the pictures and write their names in the boxes provided. There are a few letters to get you started.
B_g B_r
R_g_____
R____e

Dot-to-Dot

Who Goes There?
Rosie's very clever at finding the answers to puzzles and problems. Can you work out which picture should come next in each line?
1
2
3
4
5

Big Bear's Scrummy Snowballs

Don't despair Big Bear! Even when there's no snow you can still enjoy a snowball. This recipe makes 24 super sweet snowballs.

You will need:

24 large marshmallows,
1 tin of condensed milk,
600g of digestive biscuits,
85g shredded coconut.

What to do:

1. Put the biscuits in a sturdy plastic food bag and bash them with a rolling pin until they are crumbs.
2. Now tip them into a bowl and pour in the condensed milk. Mix well.
3. Wet your hands so the crumbs don't stick to you and roll each marshmallow in the biscuit mixture until it is coated.
4. Finally, roll each ball in the coconut to coat, and place on a plate or tray.
5. Chill in the fridge for at least 2 hours. Then eat.

Oakley's Mobile

Just because trees can't move about, it doesn't mean they should miss out on the fun. Rosie made Oakley a special telephone with a length of hose and two funnels, so he can talk to his friend Saffie in the woods. You can make a similar phone using simple instructions.

Oakley says: Needles are sharp so ask a grown-up to help.

You will need:

Two large, clean, paper cups • A length of non-stretchable, string or thread (about 30 metres) • Sticky tape (optional) • A sewing needle.

What to do:

1. Ask a grown-up to put a small hole in the bottom of each of the paper cups using the sewing needle.

2. Thread one end of the string through the bottom of one cup from outside to inside and secure with knot or tape end down.

Thread the other end of the string through the bottom of the other cup from outside to inside and secure with a knot or tape end down.

3. Now you're ready to talk. One person should take each cup and you should walk away from each other so that the string is tight between you. It should also be in a straight line. You could go into different rooms, but not if it means the string passes around corners. Try going up different ends of the garden for example.

4. Keeping the string tight, one of you should speak into the cup while the other puts their cup to their ear. They will hear everything you say. This works through the sound waves of your voice cause tiny vibrations to pass through the bottom of the cup, along the string and into the other cup.

Answers

P8–9: Everything about… Rosie
There are 10 buttons.

P10–11: Everything about… Raggles
Raggles is a RABBIT.

P12: Sunshine and Shadows
1.C; 2.F; 3.D; 4.B; 5.A; 6.E.

P13: Write it with Raggles
Holly's bow is **spotty**.
The Little Acorns love to **bounce**.
Bluebird's tail is **yellow**.

P14–15: Speedy Spot the Difference

P16–17: Happy Holly's Daisy Chain
The chain should read -
NESTWOOTERAGGLESPOTTYELLOW

P20–21: Everything about… Bluebird
The dragonfly, butterfly and ladybird can all fly. The apple cannot, it grows in trees.

P32: Acorn Hide & Seek

P34–35: Everything about… Big Bear
Big Bear has 4 paws.

P44: Muddle Trouble
1. Bluebird loves to fly.
2. Saffie is a tree.
3. Will likes playing football.
4. Rosie and Raggles ran round the roundabout.
5. Holly plays the recorder.

P45: Amazing Maze

P46–47: Everything about… Oakley
10 of Oakley's leaves have fallen.

P56–57: Aaaachhooowhose is whose?
A.4; B.5; C.1; D.2; E.3.

P59: Copy Colours
1. Holly's dress is **pink**.
2. Rosie's shoes are **red**.
3. Bluebird's beak is **pink** and **yellow**.
4. Will's trousers are **blue**.

P60: Kite Chaos
Big Bear's kite is yellow.
Little Bear's is green.
Raggles kite is blue.
Will's kite is red.

P74: Who Goes There?

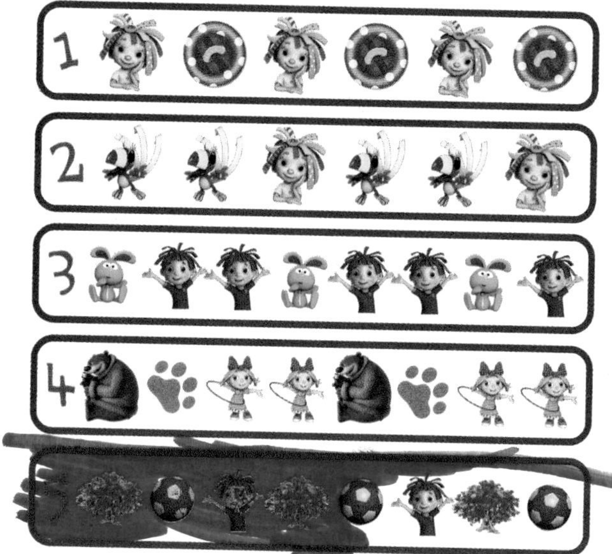